Cabins & Cottages
Design Considerations for Small Cabins & Cottages

Copyright © 2021

DEDICATION

Contents

Cedar Creek Guest House

This cozy cabin is a perfect retreat for overnight guests or weekend vacations. With a spacious porch, open floor plan, and outdoor fireplace, you may never want to leave.

BASICS

Bedrooms:1 actual,1 possible

Baths:1 full,0 half

Floors:1

Garage:0

Foundations:Slab

Primary Bedroom:

Laundry Location:

Fireplaces:1

SQUARE FOOTAGE

Main Floor:500

Total Heated Sq Ft:500

DIMENSIONS

Width x Depth:34'0" x 33'0"

Height:22'0"

PLATE HEIGHTS

Main Floor:11.0'

CONSTRUCTION

Ext. Wall Construction:2x6

Roof Framing:Gable

STYLE / INFLUENCES

Recreation/Vacation, Cabin

KITCHEN FEATURES

Open Layout

PRIMARY BEDROOM FEATURES

ADDITIONAL FEATURES

Porch, Fireplace

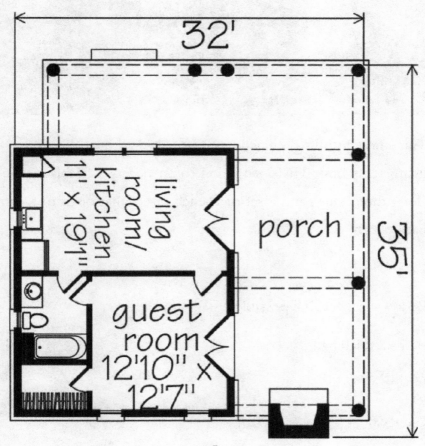

Deer Run

This thoughtfully designed and affordable house illustrates cabin living at its best. The open living room boasts a fireplace, windows along three walls, and a set of French doors that open to a screened back porch.

BASICS

Bedrooms:2 actual,2 possible

Baths:2 full,0 half

Floors:2

Garage:0

Foundations:Pier

Primary Bedroom:Main Floor

Laundry Location:Main Floor

Fireplaces:1

SQUARE FOOTAGE

Main Floor:763

Upper Floor:210

Total Heated Sq Ft:973

DIMENSIONS

Width x Depth:30'0" x 36'0"

Height:0'0"

PLATE HEIGHTS

Main Floor:8.0'

Upper Floor:8.0'

CONSTRUCTION

Ext. Wall Construction:2x4

Roof Framing: Gable

STYLE / INFLUENCES

Recreation/Vacation, Country, Southern, Cabin

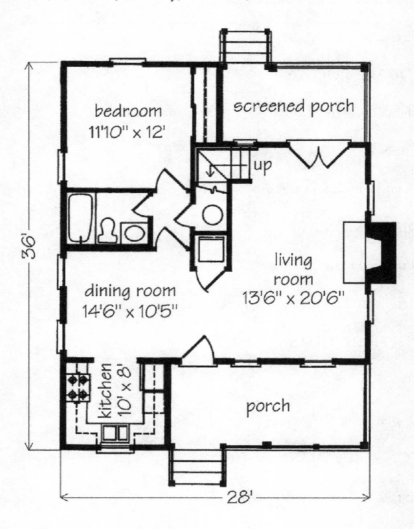

KITCHEN FEATURES

Nook

PRIMARY BEDROOM FEATURES

ADDITIONAL FEATURES

Porch, Fireplace

DESCRIPTION

Thoughtfully designed and affordable to build, this home illustrates cabin living at its best. It is the perfect hideaway for the lake or mountains, with a design that combines compactness and rustic styling.

An adorable front porch is just the place to set up a couple of chairs - or maybe a hanging swing - and take a load off your heels.

Inside, the open living room enjoys a fireplace, windows along three walls, and a set of French doors that open to a screened porch at the back. With warmth wafting over from the living room and the soothing smells of dinner being prepared in the adjoining kitchen, the dining room offers a place to settle down at the end of the day. A spacious rear bedroom makes use of the main floor's full bath.

Upstairs, a second bedroom enjoys a roomy sleeping area, plus its own private bath.

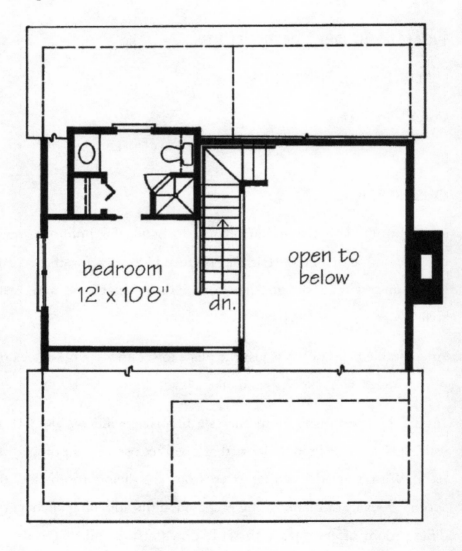

Eagle's Nest

With a touch of Gothic styling this plan offers open spaces and a straightforward layout. The main level is a multipurpose space, while the cabin's steeply pitched roof allows for a comfortable bedroom and bath upstairs. The screened back porch provides additional space.

BASICS

Bedrooms:1 actual,1 possible

Baths:1 full,1 half

Floors:2

Garage:0

Foundations:Pier

Primary Bedroom:Upper Floor

Laundry Location:Main Floor

Fireplaces:1

SQUARE FOOTAGE

Main Floor:384

Upper Floor:250

Total Heated Sq Ft:634

DIMENSIONS

Width x Depth:24'0" x 29'0"

Height:23'0"

PLATE HEIGHTS

Main Floor:9.0'

Upper Floor:8.0'

CONSTRUCTION

Ext. Wall Construction:2x4

Roof Framing:Gable

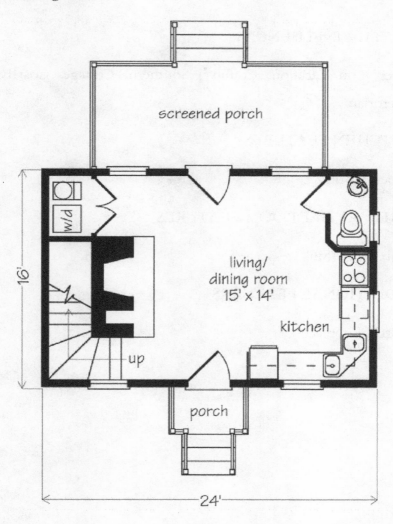

STYLE / INFLUENCES

Recreation/Vacation, Country, Southern, Cottage, Cost-Effective, Victorian

KITCHEN FEATURES

Open Layout

PRIMARY BEDROOM FEATURES

Tub, Single Sink

ADDITIONAL FEATURES

Porch, Fireplace

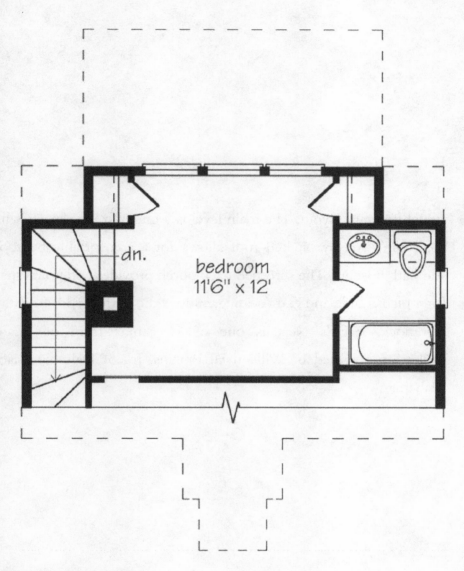

dn.

bedroom
11'6" x 12'

DESCRIPTION

Eagle's Nest offers a touch of Gothic styling with open spaces and a straightforward layout. The main level is a multipurpose space, while the cabin's steeply pitched roof allows for a comfortable bedroom and bath upstairs. The screened back porch provides additional space for a picnic table and extra seating, and it's the perfect spot to hang a hammock. Eagle's Nest is one of 16 cabins from our Cabin Collection designed by William H. Phillips, Jr., of Dauphin Island, Alabama.

Beachside Bungalow

An adorable front porch is just the place to set up a couple of chairs or maybe a hanging swing and take a load off your heels.

BASICS

Bedrooms:1 actual,1 possible

Baths:1 full,0 half

Floors:1

Garage:0

Foundations:Crawlspace

Primary Bedroom:Main Floor

Laundry Location:

Fireplaces:0

SQUARE FOOTAGE

Main Floor:484

Total Heated Sq Ft:484

DIMENSIONS

Width x Depth:23'0" x 22'0"

Height:0'0"

PLATE HEIGHTS

Main Floor:10.0'

CONSTRUCTION

Ext. Wall Construction:2x6

Roof Framing:Gable

STYLE / INFLUENCES

Bungalow, Southern, Cottage

KITCHEN FEATURES

Snack, Pantry

PRIMARY BEDROOM FEATURES

Single Sink, Tub

ADDITIONAL FEATURES

Porch

Boathouse & Bunkhouse

No place has more charm than this little boathouse perched over the water. With windows on every wall, wood siding, shuttered windows, and a metal roof with exposed rafters, this boathouse makes a welcoming weekend cottage or waterside home.

BASICS

Bedrooms:1 actual,1 possible

Baths:1 full,0 half

Floors:1

Garage:0

Foundations:Slab

Primary Bedroom:

Laundry Location:

Fireplaces:0

SQUARE FOOTAGE

Main Floor:376

Total Heated Sq Ft:376

DIMENSIONS

Width x Depth:12'0" x 32'0"

Height:14'0"

PLATE HEIGHTS

Main Floor:9.0'

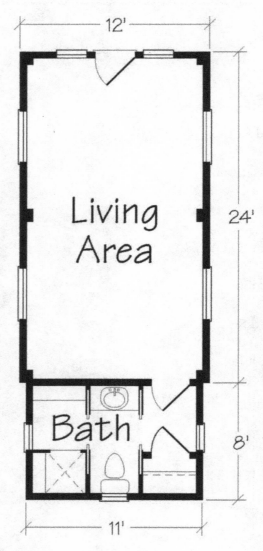

Bunk House

CONSTRUCTION

Ext. Wall Construction:2x8

Roof Framing:Gable

STYLE / INFLUENCES

Cabin, Recreation/Vacation

KITCHEN FEATURES

PRIMARY BEDROOM FEATURES

ADDITIONAL FEATURES

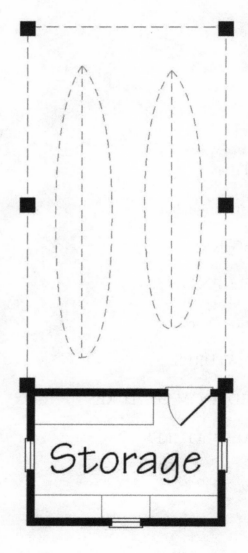

Storage

Boat House

Sun River

BASICS

Bedrooms:1 actual,1 possible

Baths:1 full,0 half

Floors:2

Garage:0

Foundations:Crawlspace, Slab

Primary Bedroom:Main Floor

Laundry Location:Main Floor

Fireplaces:0

SQUARE FOOTAGE

Main Floor:232

Upper Floor:128

Total Heated Sq Ft:360

DIMENSIONS

Width x Depth:18'0" x 22'0"

Height:20'0"

PLATE HEIGHTS

Main Floor:8.0'

Upper Floor:8.0'

CONSTRUCTION

Ext. Wall Construction:2x6

Roof Framing:Gable

STYLE / INFLUENCES

Recreation/Vacation, Country, Cabin

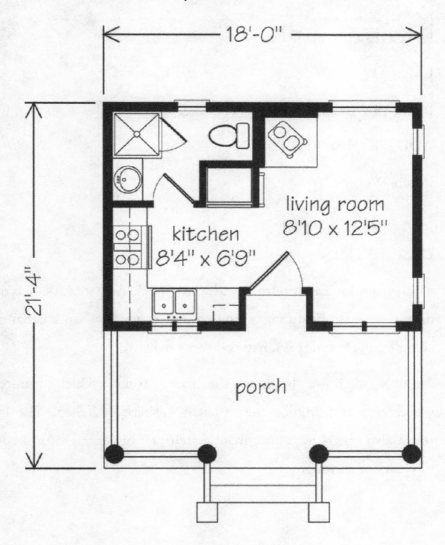

KITCHEN FEATURES

L-shaped

PRIMARY BEDROOM FEATURES

ADDITIONAL FEATURES

Porch, Woodstove

DESCRIPTION

This quaint log cabin retreat is ideal for weekend getaways or retreats in the woods. Featuring stone, rough-hewn logs and cedar roof shingles, the exterior is a nature-lover's delight.

Multiple windows brighten the living room, which features a woodstove and adjoins the efficient L-shaped kitchen. The living room also opens to roomy front porch?just big enough for a couple of chairs or a swing.

The surprisingly spacious upper-floor loft bedroom includes two sizable closets.

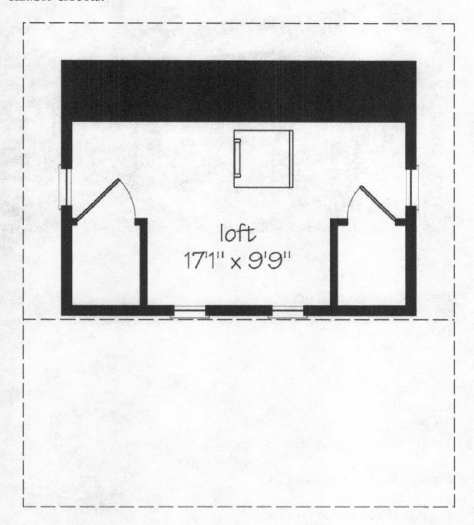

loft
17'1" x 9'9"

Yancey's Mill

BASICS

Bedrooms:1 actual,2 possible

Baths:1 full,0 half

Floors:2

Garage:0

Foundations:Crawlspace

Primary Bedroom:Main Floor

Laundry Location:Main Floor

Fireplaces:1

SQUARE FOOTAGE

Main Floor:694

Upper Floor:147

Total Heated Sq Ft:841

DIMENSIONS

Width x Depth:27'0" x 39'0"

Height:21'0"

PLATE HEIGHTS

Main Floor:9.0'

Upper Floor:7.0'

CONSTRUCTION

Ext. Wall Construction:2x4

Roof Framing:Gable

STYLE / INFLUENCES

Recreation/Vacation, Country, Southern, Cabin, Cost-Effective

KITCHEN FEATURES

Open Layout, Eat-in

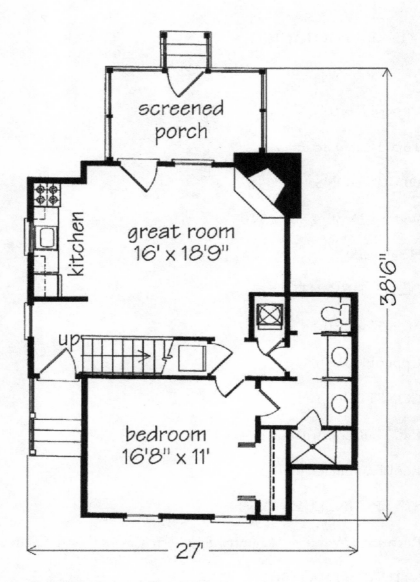

screened
porch

kitchen

great room
16' x 18'9"

up

bedroom
16'8" x 11'

38'6"

27'

PRIMARY BEDROOM FEATURES

Dual Sinks, Shower, Private Toilet

ADDITIONAL FEATURES

Porch, Fireplace

DESCRIPTION

Roughing it can be a lot of fun, as our Yancey's Mill design clearly shows. Perfect for short getaway trips or as a sportsman's cabin, it's also comfortable enough formore extended stays. The vast great room with its stone fireplace is a perfect spot to retreat after a long nature walk or leisurely boat ride. And the screened porch becomes an ideal place to grill the day's fresh catch.

Designed by William H. Phillips, Jr., of Dauphin Island, Alabama, this plan is from our Cabin Collection. The waterwheel is optional, based on site considerations.

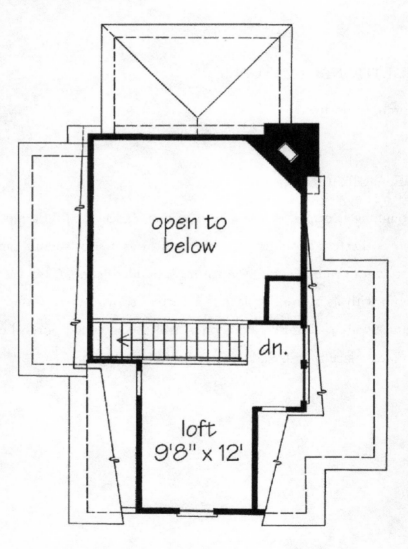

Little Red

BASICS

Bedrooms:1 actual,1 possible

Baths:1 full,0 half

Floors:2

Garage:0

Foundations:Pier

Primary Bedroom:Upper Floor

Laundry Location:Main Floor

Fireplaces:1

SQUARE FOOTAGE

Main Floor:562

Upper Floor:238

Total Heated Sq Ft:800

DIMENSIONS

Width x Depth:23'0" x 33'0"

Height:25'0"

PLATE HEIGHTS

Main Floor:9.0'

Upper Floor:8.0'

CONSTRUCTION

Ext. Wall Construction:2x6

Roof Framing:Gable

STYLE / INFLUENCES

Cost-Effective, Cabin, Southern, Recreation/Vacation, Country

KITCHEN FEATURES

Eat-in, Open Layout

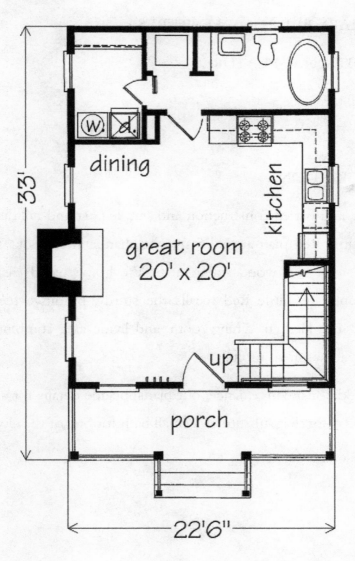

33'

dining

W. d.

kitchen

great room
20' x 20'

up

porch

22'6"

PRIMARY BEDROOM FEATURES

ADDITIONAL FEATURES

Porch, Fireplace

DESCRIPTION

Board-and-batten construction and simple post-and-rail detailing give our Little Red plan an old-fashioned, handcrafted look. The use of local stone and wood siding helps the home blend easily into its surroundings. Little Red recalls the sturdy, primitive feel of a log cabin. The kitchen, dining room, and living area combine to create one spacious great room.

For additional convenience, our plans include details for an alternate second floor that substitutes a small bath for one of the closets.

Little Red was designed by William H. Phillips, Jr., of Dauphin Island, Alabama, for our Cabin Collection.

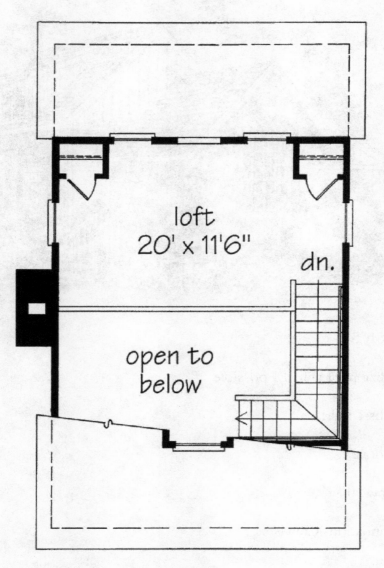

The Ozarks

BASICS

Bedrooms:1 actual,1 possible

Baths:1 full,1 half

Floors:2

Garage:0

Foundations:Crawlspace

Primary Bedroom:Upper Floor

Laundry Location:Upper Floor

Fireplaces:1

SQUARE FOOTAGE

Main Floor:680

Upper Floor:294

Total Heated Sq Ft:974

DIMENSIONS

Width x Depth:31'0" x 28'0"

Height:23'0"

PLATE HEIGHTS

Main Floor:9.0'

Upper Floor:8.0'

CONSTRUCTION

Ext. Wall Construction:2x6

Roof Framing:Gable

STYLE / INFLUENCES

Recreation/Vacation, Country, Cottage

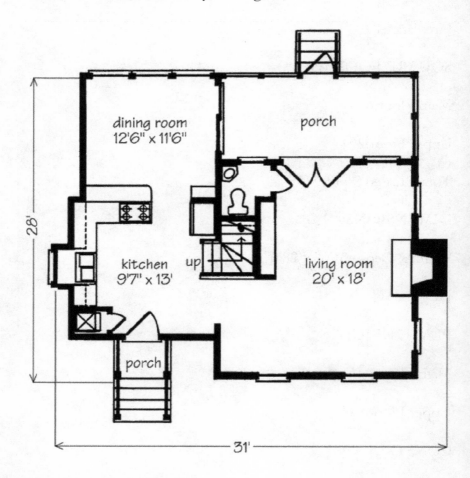

KITCHEN FEATURES

Snack, Island

PRIMARY BEDROOM FEATURES

Tub, Single Sink

ADDITIONAL FEATURES

Porch, Fireplace

DESCRIPTION

Rustic and comfortable characterize this friendly cabin called The Ozarks. Designed by architect William H. Phillips, Jr., of Dauphin Island, Alabama, the plan celebrates economy of space with less than 1,000 square feet. Overall dimensions of 31 x 28 feet enhance the cozy feel of the cabin. Doors in the living room open onto a back porch.

A spacious bedroom and bath create a private retreat upstairs.

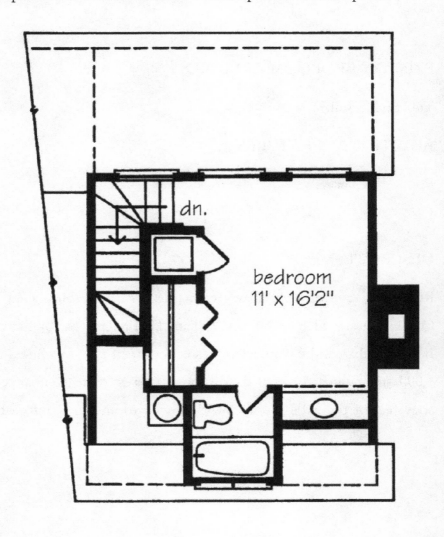

Cypress View

BASICS

Bedrooms:1 actual,1 possible

Baths:1 full,1 half

Floors:2

Garage:0

Foundations:Crawlspace

Primary Bedroom:Upper Floor

Laundry Location:Main Floor

Fireplaces:1

SQUARE FOOTAGE

Main Floor:590

Upper Floor:307

Total Heated Sq Ft:897

DIMENSIONS

Width x Depth:28'0" x 33'0"

Height:23'0"

PLATE HEIGHTS

Main Floor:9.0'

Upper Floor:8.0'

CONSTRUCTION

Ext. Wall Construction:2x4

Roof Framing:Gable

STYLE / INFLUENCES

Recreation/Vacation, Southern, Cottage, Cost-Effective

KITCHEN FEATURES

Galley

PRIMARY BEDROOM FEATURES

Walk-in Closet, Tub, Single Sink

ADDITIONAL FEATURES

Porch, Fireplace

optional
screened porch
12'8" x 8'

(dining)

kitchen
11'8" x 8'3"

great room
13'6" x 21'6"

(living)

up

porch

33'6"

28'

DESCRIPTION

Carefully planned for both enjoyment and practicality, Cypress View
is equally at home on a lake, beach, or mountain site. Designed by

William H. Phillips, Jr., of Dauphin Island, Alabama, the plan includes an optional screened porch that expands the living space and allows for enjoyment of a beautiful view. Exterior materials of board-and-batten and stacked stone are shown, but other finishes, such as lap siding and brick, may be selected to suit personal tastes, sites, or budget requirements. Cypress View is from the Southern Living Cabin Collection.

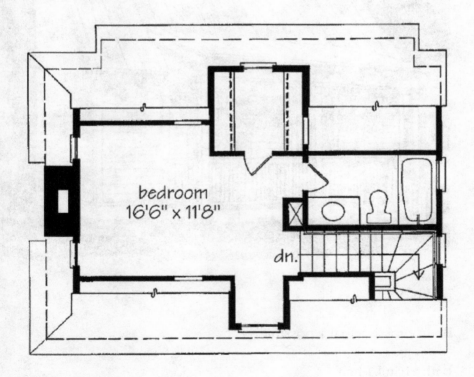

Gin Creek

BASICS

Bedrooms:1 actual,1 possible

Baths:1 full,1 half

Floors:2

Garage:0

Foundations:Crawlspace

Primary Bedroom:Upper Floor

Laundry Location:Main Floor

Fireplaces:1

SQUARE FOOTAGE

Main Floor:596

Upper Floor:310

Total Heated Sq Ft:906

DIMENSIONS

Width x Depth:30'0" x 29'0"

Height:24'0"

PLATE HEIGHTS

Main Floor:9.0'

Upper Floor:8.0'

CONSTRUCTION

Ext. Wall Construction:2x4

Roof Framing:Gable

STYLE / INFLUENCES

Recreation/Vacation, Country, Southern, Cabin, Cost-Effective

KITCHEN FEATURES

Nook

PRIMARY BEDROOM FEATURES

Shower, Tub

ADDITIONAL FEATURES

Porch, Fireplace

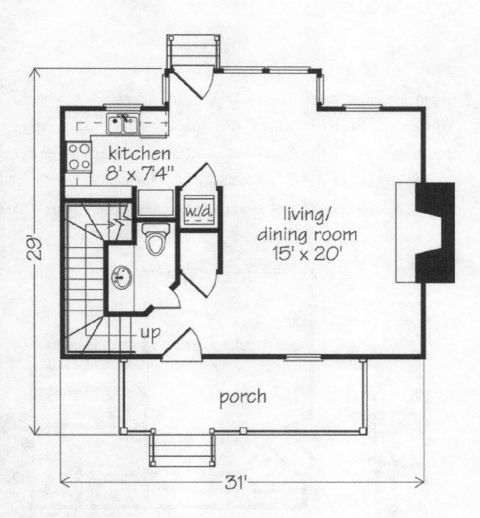

DESCRIPTION

Gin Creek is a compact, story-and-a-half cabin with enough style and flexibility to become either a lake house or a mountain retreat. A covered front porch provides a haven for afternoon naps. Inside, one room accommodates family living and dining. The kitchen is conveniently tucked behind the stairway. Upstairs, a spacious bedroom with double closets and an adjacent bath makes for a cozy, private space. Designed by William H. Phillips, Jr., of Dauphin Island, Alabama, Gin Creek is a sturdy little house that offers a blend of tradition, charm, and comfort.

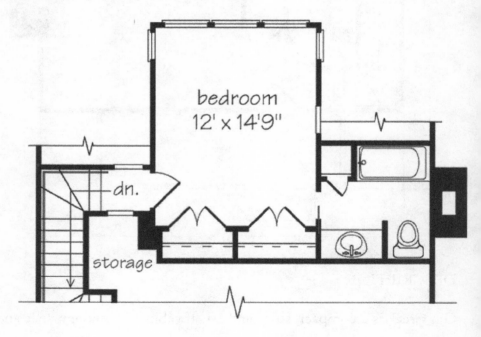

CPSIA information can be obtained
at www.ICGtesting.com
Printed in the USA
LVHW040213170723
752653LV00006B/460

9 798597 723716